Right, so you're going to
be a DAD, firstly: Congratulations
Secondly, don't worry, this Book
will cover everything you
need to know
From A MUM -TO A DAD!

WITH A BIT OF HELP
THE BEST from

DAD #1

First Published 2021

© Bethany Dempsey

Text and illustrations © Bethany Dempsey

Published and Printed by Mapseeker Digital Ltd, Unit 15, Bridgwater Court, Oldmixon Crescent, Weston Super Mare, North Somerset, BS24 9AY
Telephone +44 (0) 01922 458288 +44 (0) 7947107248

British Library Cataloguing in Publication Data
A catalogue record for this book is available from the British Library

ISBN 978-1-84491-889-8

Right....

OK....

lets Just

BREATHE

NO, NO, I said Breathe, not Hyperventilate....

Right now...

Pregnancy,

Birth,

Babies

color-coded-just
for you....

Lets Begin with ↓

PREGNANCY

first things first

you feeling ok?

Happy   emotional   Sad

chilled   ecstatic

Scared

not sure

Worried   nervous

overwhelmed

its ok to be Nervous, about, pregnancy, Birth and a Baby ....

even if it was all planned, it can still be a shock! ... and it doesn't mean you don't love your Baby ♥

Her Body is going to CHANGE...

lets go through the do's and don'ts

DO	DON'T
tell her you admire her changing body.	Say how 'BIG' she got
ask her if she needs any help (putting socks on at 8 months pregnant is hard going)	tell her to get on with it.
get her cravings at 2am...	give alternatives to cravings
nod - say aww and validate her feelings	compare your papercut to her pain
take interest in the baby & appointments	moan about anything baby related

WHOOPS

nearly missed a **very important DON'T** off that list

DO NOT HONK your Baby mamas, NEW, swollen Painful Boobies, like a Horn...

unless you want a Broken nose...?

Pregnancy is made up of

3

Trimesters

40 Weeks

weeks 1 - 12

Common symptoms, morning sickness (which can be any time), cramps, indigestion, and lots of peeing.

dating scan 12 - 14 weeks

1st Trimester

first midwife appointment around week 8-10 called a Booking appointment

This Bit is Truly Exhausting for the Baby Mama.

FIRST TRIMESTER

Nausea

Excitement

Tiredness

Nerves

1st Scan

Baby rapidly growing

Weeks 13-28

Baby Bump may begin to show in this time

dating scan 12-14 weeks

2nd Trimester

At 16 weeks a skilled sonographer can usually tell if Baby is a Boy or girl

Anomaly scan 19-20 week scan, to check for fetal abnormalities

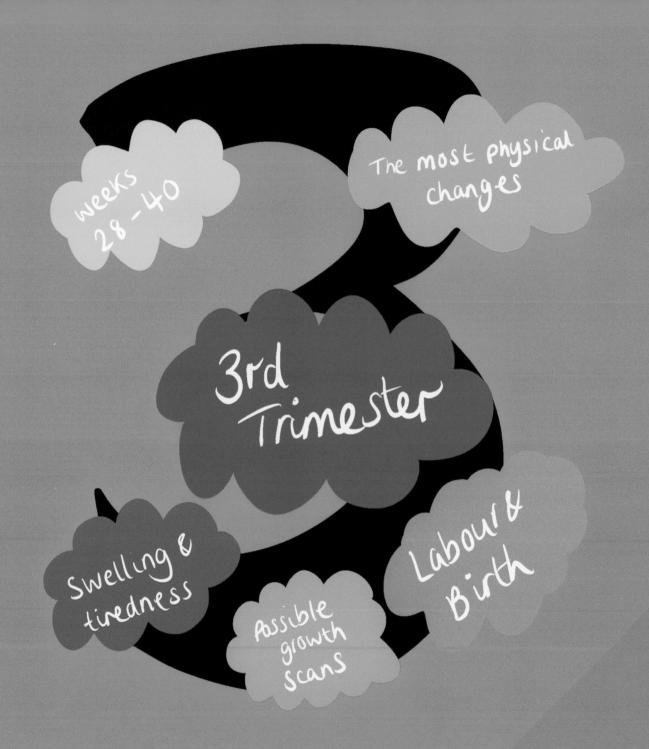

weeks 28 - 40

The most physical changes

3rd Trimester

Swelling & tiredness

Possible growth scans

Labour & Birth

THIRD TRIMESTER
exhaustion
Stretch marks
Hot sweats
nerves
cravings
labour
excited
swollen feet & ankles
Birth
rapid growth

WHAT KIND

OK SO...

SHe may go into labour
Naturally

She may have her labour
Induced

or she may have a
C-Section

OF BirtH?

Natural Birth

Spontaneous,
Can be a Water Birth,
or Home Birth 🍼
Can still need help to
Birth Baby

C-Section

C-section can be needed
for numerous medical
reasons, such as Baby in
an unusual position.
Previous C-section births
failed natural Birth.
It can Be planned or
emergency. ✡

✡ C-section
is MAJOR
surgery.

Induction

When labour is induced the aim
is still a natural Birth. mom
may be induced after due date,
if baby is showing Big or small,
medical issues such as
pre-eclampsia. Babies movement
being more or less than
usual

PACK YO BAG!

- food - not smelly or Noisy ☑
- Phone charger ☐
- Spare clothes ☐
- A Pillow ☐
- time passers / magazines ☐
- Camera ☐
- money for car park ☐
- Push present ☐
- Pain killers & drink ☐

Epsiotomy
when a mama is cut
down there to assist Birth

Ventouse
a suction cup attached
to Babies head to
help deliver Baby

Assisted Delivery...

Words
you need
to **KNOW**
& understand

forceps.
Large Salad tossers
to help grip & pull Baby
out.

THINGS SHE WANTS YOU TO KNOW

TRUST WHAT I AM SAYING! I KNOW MY BODY

DO NOT COMPLAIN ABOUT ANYTHING during labour

your snacks are NOW MY SNACKS

Stay strong you are our Biggest support ♥

if i change my mind about my Birth plan GO WITH IT!

you are gonna Be a GREAT dad!

21

TAKE ALL THE Photographs

First FEED

Just Born

As many mom + Baby pics you can

* as many unposed, no makeup pics, first moments, everything....

DILATION

established labour

1cm
CHeerio

2cm
CHerry

3cm
Banana
Slice

4cm
cracker

5cm
lime
Slice

6cm
COOKie

7cm orange
Slice

8cm Halved
apple

9cm
donut

10cm
melon

names I like...

IT'S ALL A

feeding

dressing

Winding

changing nappies

Bathing

LEARNING CURVE

so try it all! practice makes perfect

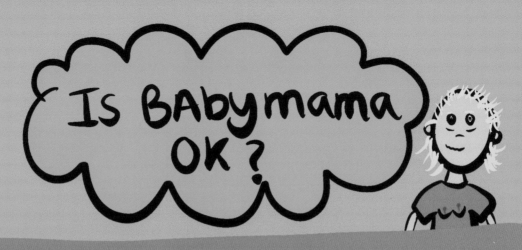

Birth is super exhausting and can be quite traumatic add in sleepless nights, hormones, pain, Healing & a Baby its ALOT, on top of that 9 months growing the baby...

MAKE HER A priority ♥

FEED THE BABY
(unless mama is breastfeeding)

SKIN TO SKIN
as early as you can
& as often as
you can

BATH THE
BABY

Bonding
Time

READ TO
THE BABY
even if they don't
understand...

Sing to the
BABY...

TAKE THE BABY
TO A CLASS.

Nappy Tip

open nappy.
close nappy super quickly
now open & change as usual.

when the air first gets to a babies
bits, it can cause them to do a wee,
so to save the wee washing your
face, we can use the tip above

#NOBODYwantsapissyface

30

Night FEEDS

If you can - SHARE THE
→ NIGHTFEEDS ←

IF YOU SHARE THE LOAD YOU
MIGHT AVOID THE
'WHO'S MORE TIRED?' ARGUMENT
& WILL CLASS AS AN ELITE DAD
ON ONLINE BABY GROUPS

IT IS PART of **DAD DUTY**
TO not only CHANGE BUT ALSO
DISPOSE of.....

>STiNKY NaPPyS<

Side note:
if you're unsure if
Baby has weed in
nappy, sometimes there is
a strip that changes
colour on the outside
of the nappy...
fancy eh?

POOP

get ready to
Talk about
poop
wayyy more
often.

Colour chart

first poop can be very dark green or black

formula fed baby poop might be abeige colour

Brown poop is common for a baby on solids

Black poop after the first 5 days can be a Sign of Blood, so let your doctor know

Breastfed baby poop can be mustard yellow

green poop isn't usually anything to worry about

red poop might be harmless but get it checked incase its blood

white or pale poop is rare but may be a Sign of liver disease so call your doctor rub the back

NO Rugby tackling

WIND THE BABY !
after EVERY feed

Gentle taps on the back

Try the baby in different Positions

Put THE REMOTE DOWN...

does the baby need anything?
do the bottles need washing...?
what about sterilising...?

Top Tip...

Baby vests mainly come with flaps on the shoulders that can be rolled down, so the vest can go down if a poonami* occurs

Poonami - A poo explosion

THE VERSATILE LIFE SAVING CLOTH

THIS IS A MUSLIN CLOTH
IT IS your new Best friend...
great to drape over your shoulder when
holding the baby (TO CATCH ANY SICK or dribble)
Perfect for mopping up spillages
might even become babies comforter

39

WHAT'S FOR TEA ?

YOU KNOW BY NOW HOW HARD, Tiring & overwhelming having a newborn is. If there's nothing for tea ORDER TAKEAWAY!

ROOKIE MISTAKE
Before sitting down with the Baby make sure everything you need is in reach.

a Hot drink

IS SHE BEING AN ARSE ?

Try not to take it too heart, this is a massive change for her aswell as you

she needs sleep

a rest

Sleep deprivation. Hormones. Pain

45

Also Available ......

ISBN 978-1-84491-883-6

£14.99

ISBN 978-1-84491-879-9

£14.99